Level 1

Lesson Assessment Book 2

Workbook

A Division of The *McGraw-Hill* Companies

SRAonline.com

An Open Court Curriculum.

Printed in the United States of America.

Send all inquiries to this address:
SRA/McGraw-Hill
4400 Easton Commons
Columbus, OH 43219-6188

ISBN: 978-0-07-613074-0
MHID: 0-07-613074-6

1 2 3 4 5 6 7 8 9 MAZ 13 12 11 10 09 08 07

The McGraw-Hill Companies

Unit 7

Unit 8

Unit 9

Unit 10

Name ______________________ Date __________ Score __________

The Kite

Comprehension and Vocabulary

Read the following questions carefully. Then completely fill in the bubble of each correct answer. You may look back at the selection to find the answer to each of the questions.

1. You know this story is not real because

Ⓐ toads can not hop.

Ⓑ kites can not fly.

Ⓒ animals can not talk.

Ⓓ birds do not land in bushes.

2. What is Toad's job?

Ⓐ to hold the ball of string

Ⓑ to hold the kite and run

Ⓒ to fix the broken kite

Ⓓ to sell the kite and string

3. What do the robins mean when they say the kite is junk?

Ⓐ The kite can fly high.

Ⓑ The kite is big and funny.

Ⓒ The kite is too fancy.

Ⓓ The kite is like trash.

The Kite (continued)

4. Why do Frog and Toad go to the meadow?

Ⓐ The wind is strong there.

Ⓑ The robins are there.

Ⓒ The kite is very big.

Ⓓ The string is very long.

5. What happens last in the story?

Ⓐ The robins fly out of the bush.

Ⓑ Frog and Toad sit and watch the kite.

Ⓒ The kite falls to the ground.

Ⓓ Toad runs back across the meadow.

6. The robins tell Toad that

Ⓐ the bush is in the way.

Ⓑ the string is too short.

Ⓒ the kite will not fly.

Ⓓ Frog is teasing him.

The Kite (continued)

7. Frog and Toad were in a **meadow.** What is a **meadow?**

Ⓐ a grassy field
Ⓑ a deep hole
Ⓒ a small pond
Ⓓ a big bush

8. The **kite** fell with a thud. What is a **kite?**

Ⓐ a pretty bug
Ⓑ a kind of plane
Ⓒ a flying toy
Ⓓ a small bird

Read the following question carefully. Use a complete sentence to answer the question.

9. Why do the robins laugh?

____

____

10. **Personal Response** Frog and Toad worked hard to fly the kite. Write about something that you worked hard to do.

____

____

____

____

The Kite (continued)

Phonics Review

Fill in the bubble under the word that fits in the blank and is spelled correctly.

1. Can we go ________?

noa	noi	nou	now
○	○	○	○

2. This is Pat's ________.

hoase	house	hoise	howse
○	○	○	○

3. Dad's ________ is sore.

knee	nee	snee	bnee
○	○	○	○

4. Sue lives ________ the street.

down	doon	doen	doun
○	○	○	○

5. The cat is ________?

uot	oot	out	oet
○	○	○	○

The Kite (continued)

Grammar, Usage, and Mechanics

Read each item. Fill in the bubble for the answer you think is correct.

1. In which sentence are commas used correctly?

Ⓐ I have a ball, bat and glove.
Ⓑ I have a ball, bat, and glove.
Ⓒ I have, a ball bat and glove.
Ⓓ I, have a, ball bat and, glove.

2. In which sentence are quotation marks used correctly?

Ⓐ Mary asked, “Will you go?”
Ⓑ Mary asked, “Will you go?
Ⓒ “Mary asked,” Will you go?
Ⓓ Mary “asked,” Will you go?

3. In which sentence are quotation marks used correctly?

Ⓐ The zoo is open, Mr. Toms said.
Ⓑ “The zoo is open, Mr. Toms said.
Ⓒ “The zoo is open,” Mr. Toms said.
Ⓓ The zoo is open, “Mr. Toms said.”

4. In which sentence are quotation marks used correctly?

Ⓐ “Come here,” Tina said.
Ⓑ Come here,” Tina said.”
Ⓒ Come here, Tina said.
Ⓓ “Come here, Tina said.

5. In which sentence are quotation marks used correctly?

Ⓐ Mom said, Clean your room now.
Ⓑ Mom said, “Clean your room now.”
Ⓒ “Mom said,” Clean your room now.
Ⓓ Mom said, Clean your room “now.”

The Kite (continued)

Oral Fluency Assessment

At the Museum

"Please, hurry," Rona said.

Aunt Dawn smiled. "I know what you want to see. You want to see the mummies."

Rona shook her head. "No. Mummies are okay, but that's not what I want to see."

Aunt Dawn kept thinking. Each time, Rona shook her head.

Then Aunt Dawn said, "I can't think of anything else."

"You know what it is? Think of all the books I have at home."

Aunt Dawn stopped to think. Then she smiled. "I know what it is." She took Rona's hand.

They went downstairs. The room they went into had huge bones and skeletons.

Rona smiled. "This is it. I love dinosaurs!"

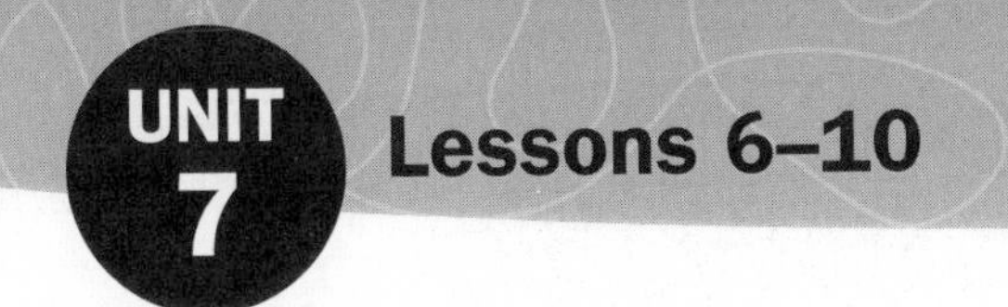

Name ______________________ Date ________ Score ________

The Little Engine That Could/Riddles

Comprehension and Vocabulary

Read the following questions carefully. Then completely fill in the bubble of each correct answer. You may look back at the selection to find the answer to each of the questions.

1. Why does the train stop?

Ⓐ People need to get off.
Ⓑ The toys need to get off.
Ⓒ The engine is not working.
Ⓓ The mountain is too tall to climb.

2. The cars of the train do NOT carry

Ⓐ dolls.
Ⓑ toy trucks.
Ⓒ food.
Ⓓ people.

3. What color is the flag the clown waves at the Shiny New Engine?

Ⓐ red
Ⓑ yellow
Ⓒ green
Ⓓ blue

The Little Engine That Could/Riddles (continued)

4. What happens right after the Little Blue Engine sees the clown?

Ⓐ She goes on ahead for help.
Ⓑ She stops at once.
Ⓒ The toys get off the train.
Ⓓ The children wake up.

5. How do we know that this story is not real?

Ⓐ Trains do not pull logs.
Ⓑ Toys do not talk.
Ⓒ Children do not like lollypops.
Ⓓ Trains do not go up mountains.

6. "Riddles" says the best riddles make you

Ⓐ thirsty.
Ⓑ hungry.
Ⓒ tired.
Ⓓ think.

The Little Engine That Could/Riddles (continued)

7. The **dining car** is a room on a train where

Ⓐ meals are served and eaten.

Ⓑ tickets are collected.

Ⓒ coal is stored.

Ⓓ people go to sleep.

8. Fine means about the same as

Ⓐ tall.

Ⓑ blue.

Ⓒ good.

Ⓓ sad.

Read the following question carefully. Use a complete sentence to answer the question.

9. How do we know the Little Blue Engine is friendly?

____

____

10. Personal Response Write about a time when you tried your best.

____

____

____

____

The Little Engine That Could/Riddles (continued)

Phonics Review

Fill in the bubble under the word that fits in the blank and is spelled correctly.

1. Ann ________ a movie last night.

swa	saw	suw	sau
○	○	○	○

2. Mom ________ a new car.

bouhgt	boght	baught	bought
○	○	○	○

3. Deb ________ the ball.

caught	cawht	cuaght	cought
○	○	○	○

4. Can the baby ________?

criwl	craul	crawl	crewl
○	○	○	○

5. Tim ran ________ he was late.

becawse	becuase	becaise	because
○	○	○	○

The Little Engine That Could/Riddles (continued)

Grammar, Usage, and Mechanics

Read each item. Fill in the bubble for the answer you think is correct.

1. In which sentence is a pronoun underlined?
   Ⓐ The cat plays <u>with</u> it.
   Ⓑ The cat <u>plays</u> with it.
   Ⓒ The cat plays with <u>it</u>.
   Ⓓ <u>The</u> cat plays with it.

2. Which sentence has a singular pronoun?
   Ⓐ I liked that movie.
   Ⓑ They went to the park.
   Ⓒ When will we pick apples?
   Ⓓ Ms. Cruz spoke to us.

3. Which sentence has a plural pronoun?
   Ⓐ We had a test today.
   Ⓑ He did not know the answer.
   Ⓒ Is she coming?
   Ⓓ The dog sat near him.

4. Which pronoun can replace the underlined part in the sentence?

   <u>Alice and Sony</u> ran the race.

   Ⓐ He
   Ⓑ She
   Ⓒ They
   Ⓓ I

5. Which pronoun can replace the underlined part in the sentence?

   Antonio kicked <u>the ball</u>.

   Ⓐ I
   Ⓑ they
   Ⓒ we
   Ⓓ it

The Little Engine That Could/Riddles (continued)

Oral Fluency Assessment

Pam's Big Day

Today was Pam's birthday. Her mom was working in the kitchen.

"Will you play with me?" Pam asked.

"Not now," Mom said.

Dad was in the basement. The door was closed.

"Don't come down now," Dad said.

"Will you play with me?" Pam asked her brother.

"Not now," Jon said. "I'm going to the store."

"Can I go with you?" Pam asked.

"Not this time," Jon said.

Pam was sad. She went to her room. She was bored.

An hour later, the doorbell rang. Pam ran downstairs. Her friend, Hank, was there. So were her friends Meg, Ron, and Amy.

"Surprise!" they shouted.

Mom brought out a cake. Dad showed up with gifts. Jon opened a bag. Inside were party hats and games.

"Happy Birthday, Pam!" everyone shouted.

Name ____________________ Date __________ Score __________

The Itsy Bitsy Spider/The Hare and the Tortoise

Comprehension and Vocabulary

Read the following questions carefully. Then completely fill in the bubble of each correct answer. You may look back at the selection to find the answer to each of the questions.

1. What happens right after the sun comes out?

Ⓐ The cat falls asleep.
Ⓑ The spider climbs a chair.
Ⓒ The rain dries up.
Ⓓ The fan turns off.

2. Which of these does the spider NOT climb?

Ⓐ the waterspout
Ⓑ the yellow pail
Ⓒ the fan
Ⓓ the maple tree

3. What makes the spider fall off the wall in the kitchen?

Ⓐ the cat
Ⓑ the rain
Ⓒ the dew
Ⓓ the fan

The Itsy Bitsy Spider/The Hare and the Tortoise (continued)

4. What do we know about the spider?
   Ⓐ The spider is always hungry.
   Ⓑ The spider does not give up.
   Ⓒ The spider is very big.
   Ⓓ The spider likes to swim.

5. Who starts the race in “The Hare and the Tortoise”?
   Ⓐ a bear
   Ⓑ a raccoon
   Ⓒ a fox
   Ⓓ a mouse

6. How does the tortoise win?
   Ⓐ He takes a shortcut.
   Ⓑ He rides in a car.
   Ⓒ He starts a long time before the hare.
   Ⓓ He passes the hare as he slept.

The Itsy Bitsy Spider/The Hare and the Tortoise (continued)

7. The hare went off at a great **pace. Pace** means
   - Ⓐ speed.
   - Ⓑ color.
   - Ⓒ sound.
   - Ⓓ size.

8. The spider spins a **silky** web. Something **silky** is
   - Ⓐ soft and smooth.
   - Ⓑ big and bumpy.
   - Ⓒ hard and slippery.
   - Ⓓ heavy and cold.

Read the following question carefully. Use a complete sentence to answer the question.

9. Why does the spider rest in the sun?

____

____

10. **Personal Response** Write about a time you had to keep trying at something.

____

____

____

____

The Itsy Bitsy Spider/The Hare and the Tortoise (continued)

Phonics Review

Fill in the bubble under the word that fits in the blank and is spelled correctly.

1. Don't make too much ________.

noyse	niose	nouse	noise
○	○	○	○

2. Beth had a new ________.

tey	toy	toiy	toi
○	○	○	○

3. Did you ________ a letter?

write	rhite	hrite	whrite
○	○	○	○

4. Grandma is on the ________.

fone	plone	phone	bhone
○	○	○	○

5. The ________ played football.

boy	bey	boi	bou
○	○	○	○

The Itsy Bitsy Spider/The Hare and the Tortoise (continued)

Grammar, Usage, and Mechanics

Read each item. Fill in the bubble for the answer you think is correct.

1. In which sentence is a possessive pronoun underlined?

Ⓐ The story was in her _book_.
Ⓑ The story was _in_ her book.
Ⓒ _The_ story was in her book.
Ⓓ The story was in _her_ book.

2. In which sentence is a possessive pronoun underlined?

Ⓐ His bike is a lot like _that_.
Ⓑ His bike is a _lot_ like that.
Ⓒ _His_ bike is a lot like that.
Ⓓ His _bike_ is a lot like that.

3. In which sentence is a possessive pronoun underlined?

Ⓐ My school is in _town_.
Ⓑ _My_ school is in town.
Ⓒ My _school_ is in town.
Ⓓ My school is _in_ town.

4. In which sentence is a possessive pronoun underlined?

Ⓐ The _dog_ played with its tail.
Ⓑ The dog played _with_ its tail.
Ⓒ The dog played with _its_ tail.
Ⓓ The dog played with its _tail_.

5. In which sentence is a possessive pronoun underlined?

Ⓐ Glen _can_ borrow my hat.
Ⓑ Glen can borrow my _hat_.
Ⓒ Glen can borrow _my_ hat.
Ⓓ Glen can _borrow_ my hat.

The Itsy Bitsy Spider/The Hare and the Tortoise (continued)

Oral Fluency Assessment

Bike Ride

"What's the matter?" Lin asked.

"Everyone is riding bikes. I want to go, too," Nate said. "But I can't ride without training wheels. No one else still has them."

"Have you tried to ride without them?" Lin asked.

Nate shook his head. "I'm too scared."

"Come on," said Lin. "I'll help you try."

Lin took off the wheels and helped Nate ride. Every day after school, Lin worked with Nate. One day, Nate got on his bike and rode all by himself. Lin clapped and cheered.

The next day, Nate said to his friends, "Let's ride bikes."

"That sounds like fun," Zach said.

Everyone else agreed. Nate hurried home to get his bike.

Name ______________________ Date __________ Score __________

Winners Never Quit!

Comprehension and Vocabulary

Read the following questions carefully. Then completely fill in the bubble of each correct answer. You may look back at the selection to find the answer to each of the questions.

1. What sport does Mia love most of all?

Ⓐ basketball
Ⓑ baseball
Ⓒ soccer
Ⓓ hockey

2. Why does Mia's team cheer?

Ⓐ Mia agrees to play.
Ⓑ Mia scores a goal.
Ⓒ Lovdy catches the ball.
Ⓓ Garrett picks Mia for his team.

3. Why does Mia quit?

Ⓐ All of the other kids are much bigger.
Ⓑ Her sister begs her to quit.
Ⓒ The ball is too soft for her.
Ⓓ She would rather quit than lose.

Winners Never Quit! (continued)

4. What happens the next day right when Mia runs outside?

Ⓐ The game has already started.

Ⓑ It begins to rain.

Ⓒ Garrett picks her for his team.

Ⓓ Mia scores a goal.

5. What does Mia learn?

Ⓐ It is a lot of fun to score goals.

Ⓑ Soccer is a lot of work.

Ⓒ Playing is more important than winning.

Ⓓ She is better at baseball than at soccer.

6. What does Mia hate?

Ⓐ playing baseball

Ⓑ blocking kicks

Ⓒ scoring a goal

Ⓓ losing

Winners Never Quit! **(continued)**

7. Mia **stomped.** This means that she
   - Ⓐ kicked a ball.
   - Ⓑ went inside.
   - Ⓒ walked heavily.
   - Ⓓ waited for the game to end.

8. **Rather** means
   - Ⓐ not.
   - Ⓑ more gladly.
   - Ⓒ always.
   - Ⓓ less time.

Read the following question carefully. Use a complete sentence to answer the question.

9. What does it mean to dribble a soccer ball?

____

____

10. **Personal Response** Write about a game you like to play very much.

____

____

____

____

Winners Never Quit! (continued)

Phonics Review

Fill in the bubble under the word that fits in the blank and is spelled correctly.

1. Min ________ them call.

haerd	heird	heard	herrd
○	○	○	○

2. Ken needs ________ for lunch.

monay	money	monee	moniy
○	○	○	○

3. The ________ is sailing off.

buot	boet	bot	boat
○	○	○	○

4. Jen ran in the ________.

race	rass	rece	rasc
○	○	○	○

5. The farmer has a ________.

muol	muule	mule	muwl
○	○	○	○

Winners Never Quit! (continued)

Grammar, Usage, and Mechanics

Read each item. Fill in the bubble for the answer you think is correct.

1. In which sentence is an adjective underlined?

Ⓐ The green grass grew in the field.

Ⓑ The green grass grew in the field.

Ⓒ The green grass grew in the field.

Ⓓ The green grass grew in the field.

2. In which sentence is an adjective underlined?

Ⓐ Five birds sat in a tree.

Ⓑ Five birds sat in a tree.

Ⓒ Five birds sat in a tree.

Ⓓ Five birds sat in a tree.

3. In which sentence is an adjective underlined?

Ⓐ Pam wore a pretty dress to the party.

Ⓑ Pam wore a pretty dress to the party.

Ⓒ Pam wore a pretty dress to the party.

Ⓓ Pam wore a pretty dress to the party.

4. Which sentence has a comparative adjective?

Ⓐ The smaller puppy is mine.

Ⓑ Did you go with him to the zoo?

Ⓒ We will go to the new store today.

Ⓓ A brown log floated in the water.

5. Which sentence has a comparative adjective?

Ⓐ Mom went to work.

Ⓑ The green frog jumped into the lake.

Ⓒ Kim is taller than Ben.

Ⓓ This book is about the moon.

Winners Never Quit! (continued)

Oral Fluency Assessment

New School

School would start tomorrow. Paul had just moved. He didn't know anyone at his new school.

That night, Dad asked, "Are you afraid?"

Paul nodded. "I don't know anyone. And I never rode a bus before."

"Do you remember being afraid to start kindergarten?" Dad asked.

Paul had felt sick then, too. "Yes," Paul whispered.

Dad hugged him. "What happened?"

"The first day I met Will and Sam. Ana shared her lunch with me. We all became friends." Paul smiled.

Dad smiled, too. "What do you think will happen tomorrow?"

Paul thought, and said, "Will the same thing happen?"

"I bet it will," Dad said and kissed Paul good night.

Name ______________________ Date ________ Score ________

Writing Prompt

Narrative Writing

Writing Situation

A time when you did something difficult

Audience

Your classmates

Directions for Writing

Think about a time when you had to try hard to succeed. It can be in school, sports, or anything else that you did. Write about what you did, how you did it, and what made you keep trying.

Checklist

You will earn the best score if you

- think about your ideas before you start writing.
- stay on topic.
- have a good beginning, middle, and end to your story.
- use describing words.
- use action words.
- tell about the place where the story happens.
- write complete sentences.
- use words that tell how you feel.
- use correct capital letters, end marks, and spelling.
- read your writing after you finish and check for mistakes.

Name ______________________ Date __________ Score __________

How a Seed Grows

Comprehension and Vocabulary

Read the following questions carefully. Then completely fill in the bubble of each correct answer. You may look back at the selection to find the answer to each of the questions.

1. Which of these does NOT grow from seeds?

Ⓐ apple tree
Ⓑ bird
Ⓒ corn
Ⓓ clover

2. What do you do right after you make a hole in the soil?

Ⓐ Fill in the hole.
Ⓑ Put water on the soil.
Ⓒ Write a number on the shell.
Ⓓ Put one seed in the hole.

3. Why can't you see the seeds begin to grow?

Ⓐ They are too small.
Ⓑ They do not have enough water.
Ⓒ They are under the soil.
Ⓓ They are broken.

How a Seed Grows (continued)

4. Which of these is a kind of bean?

Ⓐ pole
Ⓑ clover
Ⓒ wheat
Ⓓ apple

5. Why were twelve seeds planted in the story?

Ⓐ so we can start a garden
Ⓑ so we can see the seeds grow
Ⓒ so we can get many plants
Ⓓ so we can use many beans

6. How are all seeds alike?

Ⓐ All seeds make beans.
Ⓑ All seeds are very tiny.
Ⓒ All seeds need soil to grow.
Ⓓ All seeds are good to eat.

How a Seed Grows (continued)

7. The growing seed pushes soil **aside. Aside** means
   - Ⓐ to one side.
   - Ⓑ to the inside.
   - Ⓒ into the air.
   - Ⓓ into the ground.

8. The **root** grows from one part of the bean seed. What is a **root?**
   - Ⓐ a kind of bean
   - Ⓑ a part of a plant which grows into the ground
   - Ⓒ a part of a plant which holds up the leaves
   - Ⓓ a small insect

Read the following question carefully. Use a complete sentence to answer the question.

9. What is the difference between how an oak tree grows and how a bean plant grows?

____

____

10. **Personal Response** Write about a garden you know. It can be your garden or a garden you have seen.

____

____

____

How a Seed Grows (continued)

Phonics Review

Fill in the bubble under the word that fits in the blank and is spelled correctly.

1. Did they ________ the floors?

wix	wex	wax	wox
○	○	○	○

2. This is the ________ book I read.

same	saam	samm	saim
○	○	○	○

3. The officer has a ________.

bedge	bidge	bodge	badge
○	○	○	○

4. The rice came in a ________.

saack	sack	soack	seck
○	○	○	○

5. It looks like ________.

ran	rian	rain	raine
○	○	○	○

How a Seed Grows (continued)

Grammar, Usage, and Mechanics

Read each item. Fill in the bubble for the answer you think is correct.

1. Which of these is a telling sentence?

Ⓐ What day is today?
Ⓑ Who is coming tomorrow?
Ⓒ Lin swims in the lake.
Ⓓ This is a great game!

2. Which of these is a telling sentence?

Ⓐ How many children are there?
Ⓑ Mike climbs a tall tree.
Ⓒ Where is the door?
Ⓓ When will we leave?

3. Which of these is an asking sentence?

Ⓐ Give your brother a turn.
Ⓑ Whose book is this?
Ⓒ Jan rides her bike.
Ⓓ Kick it over here!

4. Which of these is an asking sentence?

Ⓐ Is Lisa at home?
Ⓑ The tiger hid in the grass.
Ⓒ Do not drop that!
Ⓓ That is a funny story.

5. Which of these is an asking sentence?

Ⓐ Dad washed the dishes.
Ⓑ Don't forget your coat!
Ⓒ Is that hat mine?
Ⓓ Paul set the table.

How a Seed Grows (continued)

Oral Fluency Assessment

At the Library

Dana loved the library. Mom and Dad took her to there every Saturday. Dana got to choose her own books.

One day, Dana found a good book. She showed her mom the book.

"Look," Dana said. "It's *Little House in the Big Woods.*"

Mom said, "I loved that book when I was a little girl."

Dana was surprised. "You read this book?" she said. "But you're old!"

Mom laughed. "Yes, but that book is older."

Dana turned to her father and asked, "What books did you like to read?"

Dad said, "I read books about sports. Then I read adventure books. I still like to read books like that."

Mom laughed and said, "I guess that means you never grew up."

Name ______________________ Date ________ Score ________

The Garden/Saguaro

Comprehension and Vocabulary

Read the following questions carefully. Then completely fill in the bubble of each correct answer. You may look back at the selection to find the answer to each of the questions.

1. Which of these does Toad NOT try so his seeds will grow?

Ⓐ digging them up
Ⓑ shouting at them
Ⓒ playing music for them
Ⓓ reading poems to them

2. What does Toad want to have?

Ⓐ a home
Ⓑ a garden
Ⓒ a tree
Ⓓ a meal

3. Why do Toad's seeds not grow when he wants them to grow?

Ⓐ He has not given them enough water.
Ⓑ The seeds are dead.
Ⓒ The seeds he planted are not real.
Ⓓ He has not waited long enough.

The Garden/Saguaro (continued)

4. Why does Toad fall asleep?

Ⓐ He ran a long way.

Ⓑ He ate a big meal.

Ⓒ He worked hard.

Ⓓ Frog makes him take a nap.

5. A saguaro is a kind of

Ⓐ animal.

Ⓑ weed.

Ⓒ cactus.

Ⓓ tree.

6. What is inside a saguaro?

Ⓐ water

Ⓑ sand

Ⓒ dirt

Ⓓ rocks

The Garden/Saguaro (continued)

7. "**Quite** soon," said Frog. **Quite** means
   Ⓐ not.
   Ⓑ very.
   Ⓒ later.
   Ⓓ always.

8. Toad **shouted** at his seeds. **Shouted** means
   Ⓐ called loudly.
   Ⓑ planted.
   Ⓒ looked carefully.
   Ⓓ listened.

Read the following question carefully. Use a complete sentence to answer the question.

9. Where does Toad get seeds for his garden?

____

____

10. **Personal Response** Write about something that was hard for you to wait for.

____

____

____

____

The Garden/Saguaro (continued)

Phonics Review

Fill in the bubble under the word that fits in the blank and is spelled correctly.

1. Wes is very ________.

sicke	soick	sick	seck
○	○	○	○

2. That dog is ________.

mine	mene	minn	mone
○	○	○	○

3. Can Dad ________ this?

fixe	fex	faix	fix
○	○	○	○

4. Please do not ________.

crie	cre	cra	cry
○	○	○	○

5. The rope was ________.

taed	tied	tiyd	teid
○	○	○	○

The Garden/Saguaro (continued)

Grammar, Usage, and Mechanics

Read each item. Fill in the bubble for the answer you think is correct.

1. In which sentence is a possessive noun underlined?

Ⓐ Jen's dog barks loudly.

Ⓑ Jen's dog barks loudly.

Ⓒ Jen's dog barks loudly.

Ⓓ Jen's dog barks loudly.

2. In which sentence is a possessive noun underlined?

Ⓐ The cat's tail is white.

Ⓑ The cat's tail is white.

Ⓒ The cat's tail is white.

Ⓓ The cat's tail is white.

3. Which sentence has a singular possessive pronoun?

Ⓐ The boy ran down the hill.

Ⓑ That is her toy.

Ⓒ The cars are red and black.

Ⓓ A bug is on the plant.

4. Which sentence has a singular possessive pronoun?

Ⓐ I lost my bag a few days ago.

Ⓑ The toys are in the closet.

Ⓒ Those girls like to climb trees.

Ⓓ He is looking for the kitten.

5. Which sentence has a plural possessive pronoun?

Ⓐ The fish swim in the water.

Ⓑ Horses have strong legs.

Ⓒ Mom put our lunches in the box.

Ⓓ The ball rolled down the hill.

The Garden/Saguaro (continued)

Oral Fluency Assessment

A Walk in the Park

It was a nice day. Ben went for a walk in the park. The park was near his home. The park has grass and trees. There is a pretty lake in the park. There are benches near the lake.

Ben heard a noise. He looked up and saw a nest. It was in a tree in the park. Then he saw a pretty bird fly to the tree. The bird landed near the nest. Ben hoped there were baby birds in the nest. He wanted to see the baby birds grow up. Ben would come back to the park again to see the baby birds.

Name ______________________ **Date** ________ **Score** ________

Green and Growing

Comprehension and Vocabulary

Read the following questions carefully. Then completely fill in the bubble of each correct answer. You may look back at the selection to find the answer to each of the questions.

1. Which of these is NOT a plant?

Ⓐ a tree
Ⓑ a shrub
Ⓒ a butterfly
Ⓓ a vine

2. How are all green growing things alike?

Ⓐ They all make their own food.
Ⓑ They all move around to find water.
Ⓒ They all have cones.
Ⓓ They all have stems.

3. What is the smallest plant on Earth?

Ⓐ redwood
Ⓑ cedar
Ⓒ cattail
Ⓓ duckweed

Green and Growing (continued)

4. Which of these are parts of a plant?
- Ⓐ roots, leaves
- Ⓑ fir, cedar
- Ⓒ poppies, daisies
- Ⓓ cactus, reed

5. Where does a lily of the valley grow best?
- Ⓐ on a rocky hill
- Ⓑ in a cool, dark place
- Ⓒ on a mountain slope
- Ⓓ in a hot, dry desert

6. A way plants move is by
- Ⓐ bending away from ice.
- Ⓑ sliding down hills.
- Ⓒ growing toward sunlight.
- Ⓓ jumping into water.

Green and Growing (continued)

7. Plants give us **energy. Energy** is
   - Ⓐ a fancy flower.
   - Ⓑ the air we breathe.
   - Ⓒ the strength to do something.
   - Ⓓ a kind of wood.

8. A **shrub** is a kind of
   - Ⓐ bush.
   - Ⓑ pond.
   - Ⓒ food.
   - Ⓓ paper.

Read the following question carefully. Use a complete sentence to answer the question.

9. How tall can a giant redwood tree be?

____

____

10. **Personal Response** What plants do you like?

____

____

____

____

____

Green and Growing (continued)

Phonics Review

Fill in the bubble under the word that fits in the blank and is spelled correctly.

1. Look at that big ________!

rock	rocke	reck	ruck
○	○	○	○

2. Put out the fire with the ________.

hoss	hose	hise	hase
○	○	○	○

3. What is in this ________?

boxe	bax	box	bix
○	○	○	○

4. Mom cut the ________ of bread.

loaf	liaf	leif	luaf
○	○	○	○

5. It is time to go ________.

homm	hame	hime	home
○	○	○	○

Green and Growing (continued)

Grammar, Usage, and Mechanics

Read each item. Fill in the bubble for the answer you think is correct.

1. Which word means about the same as bake?
   - Ⓐ eat
   - Ⓑ fly
   - Ⓒ cook
   - Ⓓ swim

2. Which word means about the same as discover?
   - Ⓐ find
   - Ⓑ run
   - Ⓒ send
   - Ⓓ drive

3. Which word means about the same as tiny?
   - Ⓐ sick
   - Ⓑ small
   - Ⓒ true
   - Ⓓ large

4. Which word means about the same as start?
   - Ⓐ turn
   - Ⓑ hide
   - Ⓒ begin
   - Ⓓ read

5. Which word means about the same as beautiful?
   - Ⓐ small
   - Ⓑ pretty
   - Ⓒ happy
   - Ⓓ wet

Green and Growing (continued)

Oral Fluency Assessment

Best Friends

A man and his dog were in the park. They were playing in a large, grassy field. The man threw the ball. The dog ran after the ball. The dog brought the ball back to the man. The dog wagged its tail. It was having a lot of fun. The man looked like he was having fun, too.

The man and the dog finished playing their game. Then they went for a walk. The dog was very good. He walked right next to the man. The dog did not pull at the leash. All the people who saw them could tell that they were happy. They could see that the man and the dog were best friends.

Name ______________________ **Date** __________ **Score** __________

Flowers/Flowers at Night

Comprehension and Vocabulary

Read the following questions carefully. Then completely fill in the bubble of each correct answer. You may look back at the selection to find the answer to each of the questions.

1. Plants need flowers to make

Ⓐ roots.

Ⓑ seeds.

Ⓒ stems.

Ⓓ bugs.

2. Flowers begin as

Ⓐ buds.

Ⓑ roots.

Ⓒ sticks.

Ⓓ leaves.

3. Birds and bugs both use flowers to

Ⓐ hide in them.

Ⓑ drink nectar from them.

Ⓒ make perfume from them.

Ⓓ match the color of them.

Flowers/Flowers at Night (continued)

4. Where do the flowers of a plant grow?
- Ⓐ under the ground
- Ⓑ on the roots
- Ⓒ at the end of a stem
- Ⓓ inside a seed

5. The first part of "Flowers at Night" is about flowers that
- Ⓐ are yellow.
- Ⓑ close up at night.
- Ⓒ bugs like.
- Ⓓ grow very tall.

6. Flowers in the poem are compared to
- Ⓐ rainbows.
- Ⓑ pretty feathers.
- Ⓒ open windows.
- Ⓓ butterflies.

Flowers/Flowers at Night (continued)

7. Flowers are **bright. Bright** is another word for
   Ⓐ smelly.
   Ⓑ large.
   Ⓒ beautiful.
   Ⓓ colorful.

8. Flowers have **petals.** What are **petals**?
   Ⓐ the part of a flower that has color
   Ⓑ the part of the flower that holds it up
   Ⓒ the part of the flower that makes seeds
   Ⓓ the part of the flower that takes in sunlight

Read the following question carefully. Use a complete sentence to answer the question.

9. What is true about all of the flowers on one plant?

____

____

10. **Personal Response** Where can you see pretty flowers where you live?

____

____

____

____

Flowers/Flowers at Night (continued)

Phonics Review

Fill in the bubble under the word that fits in the blank and is spelled correctly.

1. Laura wished us ________.

leck	lucke	lyck	luck
○	○	○	○

2. Do you want an ice ________?

cabe	cuub	cube	cibe
○	○	○	○

3. Mary could not ________ the log.

budge	bedge	bidge	bodje
○	○	○	○

4. There are a ________ grapes left.

fu	few	fue	faw
○	○	○	○

5. May I play some ________ now?

mesic	masic	mosic	music
○	○	○	○

Flowers/Flowers at Night (continued)

Grammar, Usage, and Mechanics

Read each item. Fill in the bubble for the answer you think is correct.

1. Which word means the opposite of hard?

Ⓐ easy
Ⓑ small
Ⓒ pretty
Ⓓ fast

2. Which word means the opposite of leave?

Ⓐ see
Ⓑ laugh
Ⓒ come
Ⓓ drop

3. Which word means the opposite of young?

Ⓐ old
Ⓑ mad
Ⓒ lost
Ⓓ hard

4. Which word means the opposite of less?

Ⓐ kind
Ⓑ more
Ⓒ nice
Ⓓ funny

5. Which word means the opposite of good?

Ⓐ free
Ⓑ tall
Ⓒ bad
Ⓓ dry

Flowers/Flowers at Night (continued)

Oral Fluency Assessment

Brownie's Turn

It was a warm day. The sun was shining. Dot was playing outside. She saw her friend, Ken. This gave her an idea.

"Do you want to play tag?" asked Dot. Ken said he did. They looked for more friends. That way the game would be more fun.

They went to Pat's house. She said she would play. Her brother, Mark, wanted to play, too.

The four children went to Dot's yard. They were all set to play. Then Ken's dog, Brownie, ran into the yard. The children laughed. Brownie wanted to play tag with them, too.

Name ______________________ Date ________ Score ________

Plants That Eat Animals

Comprehension and Vocabulary

Read the following questions carefully. Then completely fill in the bubble of each correct answer. You may look back at the selection to find the answer to each of the questions.

1. Where do most plants get what they need to grow?

Ⓐ from the air
Ⓑ from the soil
Ⓒ from its flowers
Ⓓ from people

2. What do the leaves of a Venus flytrap look like?

Ⓐ a bat's wing
Ⓑ a cat's tail
Ⓒ a clam's shell
Ⓓ a dog's nose

3. What happens right after an insect touches the hairs on a Venus flytrap leaf?

Ⓐ The halves of the leaf snap shut.
Ⓑ The leaf gives off a sweet smell.
Ⓒ The plant grows very tall.
Ⓓ The plant removes minerals from the insect.

Plants That Eat Animals (continued)

4. What makes the hairs on a sundew leaf fold over?

Ⓐ rain falling on the plant
Ⓑ sun hitting the plant
Ⓒ an insect getting stuck on the plant
Ⓓ a person touching the plant

5. Why is the insect stuck in the pitcher plant?

Ⓐ It cannot climb back up the slippery sides.
Ⓑ The liquid inside the plant is sticky.
Ⓒ A leaf of the plant folds over.
Ⓓ The plant sucks the insect inside.

6. Which of these is a plant that eats animals?

Ⓐ a bladderwort
Ⓑ a tulip
Ⓒ a bamboo
Ⓓ a dandelion

Plants That Eat Animals (continued)

7. Some plants live in **wetlands. Wetlands** are
   Ⓐ mountains.
   Ⓑ deserts.
   Ⓒ forests.
   Ⓓ swamps.

8. The leaf gives off a sweet juice that **insects** like. **Insects** are
   Ⓐ animals with fur.
   Ⓑ fish with scales.
   Ⓒ bugs with six legs.
   Ⓓ animals with long tails.

Read the following question carefully. Use a complete sentence to answer the question.

9. How did the pitcher plant get its name?

____

____

10. **Personal Response** What plant do you like best? Why do you like it?

____

____

____

____

Plants That Eat Animals (continued)

Phonics Review

Fill in the bubble under the word that fits in the blank and is spelled correctly.

1. Dan took a ________ of the apple.

bite	bote	baite	biit
○	○	○	○

2. Wash the dishes with ________.

seop	soop	soap	soip
○	○	○	○

3. The boys ________ to go fishing.

hop	hupe	hape	hope
○	○	○	○

4. Some pigs are ________.

houg	huge	hage	hige
○	○	○	○

5. A cat will ________ a mouse.

chese	chase	chaas	chise
○	○	○	○

Plants That Eat Animals (continued)

Grammar, Usage, and Mechanics

Read each item. Fill in the bubble for the answer you think is correct.

1. Which of these means the same as is not?
   Ⓐ it's
   Ⓑ can't
   Ⓒ isn't
   Ⓓ hasn't

2. Which of these means the same as we will?
   Ⓐ we've
   Ⓑ we're
   Ⓒ we'll
   Ⓓ she'll

3. Which of these means the same as they are?
   Ⓐ he's
   Ⓑ they're
   Ⓒ that's
   Ⓓ here's

4. Which of these means the same as wasn't?
   Ⓐ would not
   Ⓑ will not
   Ⓒ was not
   Ⓓ were not

5. Which of these means the same as I'm?
   Ⓐ I am
   Ⓑ I will
   Ⓒ I did
   Ⓓ I might

Plants That Eat Animals (continued)

Oral Fluency Assessment

Worming Around

Worms live underground most of the time. They dig holes deep in the ground. The holes help plants grow. The holes help worms, too. They give the worms a place to hide.

Sometimes worms come out of the ground at night. They do this on warm, wet nights. You might see worms on the ground after a spring rain. They like the ground to be wet.

Birds like to eat worms. They look for the worms early in the day. Did you ever hear someone say, "The early bird gets the worm"? That's where this saying comes from.

Name ______________________ Date ________ Score ________

Writing Prompt

Expository Writing

Writing Situation

A tree or other plant near where you live

Audience

A friend or family member your age who lives in a different place

Directions for Writing

Think about a tree or other plant near where you live. It can be a huge tree in a park, a plant with flowers near where you live, or any other plant that you know. Write about the plant in a way that will help the person who reads your story understand what the plant looks like and what is interesting about it.

Checklist

You will earn the best score if you

- choose a plant that you know well.
- think about the plant before you start writing.
- remember who will read about your plant.
- use describing words to tell about the plant.
- write paragraphs that have a topic sentence and focus on related ideas.
- write complete sentences.
- use words that tell how you feel about the plant.
- use correct capital letters, end marks, and spelling.
- read your writing after you finish and check for mistakes.

Name ________________ Date ________ Score ________

Homes

Comprehension and Vocabulary

Read the following questions carefully. Then completely fill in the bubble of each correct answer. You may look back at the selection to find the answer to each of the questions.

1. What is a home in the Arctic made of?

Ⓐ clay and mud
Ⓑ snow and ice
Ⓒ sticks and branches
Ⓓ cloth and blankets

2. Why is grass on the roof of a house woven tightly?

Ⓐ to keep out rain
Ⓑ to keep out sunshine
Ⓒ to keep the house cool
Ⓓ to keep birds from getting in

3. What is the same about all homes?

Ⓐ They are made of wood.
Ⓑ They are easy to build.
Ⓒ They give us shelter.
Ⓓ They can be carried.

Homes (continued)

4. Which of these would be good to use to build a home you could move easily?

Ⓐ ice
Ⓑ clay
Ⓒ blankets
Ⓓ bricks

5. What would be a problem for a home made of packed mud?

Ⓐ wind
Ⓑ rain
Ⓒ heat
Ⓓ cold

6. What is the same about what people use to make their homes?

Ⓐ They use cement.
Ⓑ They use expensive tools.
Ⓒ They use only wood.
Ⓓ They use what is at hand.

Homes (continued)

7. Homes in the desert are made of **clay.** What is **clay?**
   Ⓐ soft, sticky mud
   Ⓑ animal skins
   Ⓒ sand and rocks
   Ⓓ the inside of a cactus

8. Good houses are **sturdy.** What does **sturdy** mean?
   Ⓐ pretty
   Ⓑ tall
   Ⓒ wide
   Ⓓ strong

Read the following question carefully. Use a complete sentence to answer the question.

9. Why do people who move from place to place have simple homes?

____

____

10. **Personal Response** Write about your home and what you like most about it.

____

____

____

____

Homes (continued)

Phonics Review

Fill in the bubble under the word that fits in the blank and is spelled correctly.

1. Let's go out on the ________.

decke	dack	deeke	deck
○	○	○	○

2. We heard a ________.

bep	beep	bapp	bipe
○	○	○	○

3. The children rode ________.

ponies	ponees	poneis	ponais
○	○	○	○

4. It's Ron's turn ________.

next	naxt	noxt	nixt
○	○	○	○

5. Bees make ________.

honie	honay	honey	honee
○	○	○	○

Homes (continued)

Grammar, Usage, and Mechanics

Read each item. Fill in the bubble for the answer you think is correct.

1. Which sentence is in the present tense?

Ⓐ Emma feeds her dog.

Ⓑ Her dog wanted more food.

Ⓒ Emma walked her dog.

Ⓓ The dog liked the walk.

2. Which sentence is in the present tense?

Ⓐ The man chopped the tree.

Ⓑ Ron plays in the park.

Ⓒ The flowers looked pretty.

Ⓓ A rabbit hopped on the log.

3. Which sentence is in the past tense?

Ⓐ Finn runs in a race.

Ⓑ Mary swims in the pool.

Ⓒ Bill jumped over a rock.

Ⓓ Tina throws a ball.

4. Which sentence is in the past tense?

Ⓐ Three children played tag.

Ⓑ My brother helps Dad clean.

Ⓒ My sister rakes the leaves.

Ⓓ Our friend says hello.

5. Which sentence is in the past tense?

Ⓐ Mom works in the garden.

Ⓑ We planted peas and beans.

Ⓒ Dads pulls out weeds.

Ⓓ Leaves grow on the trees.

Homes (continued)

Oral Fluency Assessment

Socks and String

Socks heard a loud noise. He was afraid.

He ran under the bed and hid. He did not want to come out.

"I'm sorry," said Kim. She looked under the bed at her kitten. "I dropped my book. Please don't be afraid."

Socks did not understand Kim. He did not know what she was saying. He was still afraid. He did not want to come out from under the bed.

Kim had an idea. She got a piece of string. The string was Socks's favorite toy. Quick as a wink, Socks forgot he was afraid. He wanted to play with the string.

Name ______________________ Date ________ Score ________

Homes Around the World/Building a House

Comprehension and Vocabulary

Read the following questions carefully. Then completely fill in the bubble of each correct answer. You may look back at the selection to find the answer to each of the questions.

1. What kind of home folds up?

Ⓐ a pueblo
Ⓑ a tent
Ⓒ a reed hut
Ⓓ a house on stilts

2. What are all the homes in this story used for?

Ⓐ All of them float.
Ⓑ All of them are on wheels.
Ⓒ All of them are for living.
Ⓓ All of them are made of plants

3. In Mali, houses are cool on hot days because

Ⓐ they have windows.
Ⓑ they are built in cliffs.
Ⓒ they have water all around.
Ⓓ they do not have roofs.

Homes Around the World/Building a House (continued)

4. A window is most like
- Ⓐ a wheel.
- Ⓑ a door.
- Ⓒ a fireplace.
- Ⓓ a roof.

5. Who helps build a house?
- Ⓐ a cook
- Ⓑ a teacher
- Ⓒ a plumber
- Ⓓ a nurse

6. How is an electrician like a plumber?
- Ⓐ They do their jobs after the roof is on.
- Ⓑ The walls need to be up before they can do their jobs.
- Ⓒ The house needs to be painted before they can do their jobs.
- Ⓓ They do their jobs before the cement is poured.

Homes Around the World/Building a House (continued)

7. Sidewalks are made of **cement.** What is **cement?**

Ⓐ the new roof
Ⓑ big pieces of wood
Ⓒ sand, water, and rock
Ⓓ a kind of wire

8. A **porch** is a nice place to sit. A **porch** is

Ⓐ a place covered with flowers.
Ⓑ the back of a floating home.
Ⓒ for people to smile out of.
Ⓓ an entrance covered with a roof.

Read the following question carefully. Use a complete sentence to answer the question.

9. Why do people have windows?

____

____

10. Personal Response What kind of house do you want to live in? Why?

____

____

____

____

Homes Around the World/Building a House (continued)

Phonics Review

Fill in the bubble under the word that fits in the blank and is spelled correctly.

1. Beth took one ________.

snep	step	shep	slep
○	○	○	○

2. Her cat is ________.

brack	blak	black	blask
○	○	○	○

3. We saw a ________ by the sea.

crab	clab	srab	chab
○	○	○	○

4. Do not ________ the paint.

brip	dlip	dhip	drip
○	○	○	○

5. What is your ________?

plan	phan	slan	pran
○	○	○	○

Homes Around the World/Building a House (continued)

Grammar, Usage, and Mechanics

Read each item. Fill in the bubble for the answer you think is correct.

1. Which sentence is in the past tense?
   - Ⓐ Dad carried the big box.
   - Ⓑ The box has a bow on it.
   - Ⓒ It is a present for Grandma.
   - Ⓓ Grandma lives near us.

2. Which sentence is in the past tense?
   - Ⓐ The baby cried for its bottle.
   - Ⓑ The mother holds the baby.
   - Ⓒ The baby drinks juice.
   - Ⓓ The father helps, too.

3. Which sentence is in the past tense?
   - Ⓐ Amy's cat sits on her lap.
   - Ⓑ Kitty reads a book.
   - Ⓒ Jon ate his cereal.
   - Ⓓ Fran listens to the radio.

4. Which sentence is in the past tense?
   - Ⓐ Aaron saw his father.
   - Ⓑ Jim talks to us on the phone.
   - Ⓒ Aunt Rita cooks breakfast.
   - Ⓓ The phone rings.

5. Which sentence is in the past tense?
   - Ⓐ The lion sleeps in the sun.
   - Ⓑ The tiger roared at a mouse.
   - Ⓒ The monkey hangs in a tree.
   - Ⓓ The bear looks for fish.

Homes Around the World/Building a House (continued)

Oral Fluency Assessment

The Circus Comes Home

Lynn's friends invited her to go to the circus. It was in a big tent. The tent was full of people. There was music playing.

Three large rings were in the middle of the tent. There were acts in each ring. Lynn did not know where to look first. She loved the bears. Her friends liked the clowns best.

The next day, the girls played circus. They put a sheet on chairs. This was their tent. They made believe they were part of the acts. Some girls were clowns. Others were animals. Lynn's mom made them snacks. She said they had a great circus. She asked if she could watch.

Name ____________________ Date ________ Score ________

The White House/Snail's Pace

Comprehension and Vocabulary

Read the following questions carefully. Then completely fill in the bubble of each correct answer. You may look back at the selection to find the answer to each of the questions.

1. The first president to live in the White House was
- Ⓐ George Washington.
- Ⓑ John Adams.
- Ⓒ Abraham Lincoln.
- Ⓓ Thomas Jefferson.

2. In which city is the White House?
- Ⓐ Washington, D.C.
- Ⓑ New York
- Ⓒ Philadelphia
- Ⓓ Boston

3. Where in the White House does the president work?
- Ⓐ the East Room
- Ⓑ the Blue Room
- Ⓒ the Blue Office
- Ⓓ the Oval Office

The White House/Snail's Pace (continued)

4. What is the name of the largest room in the White House?

Ⓐ the East Room

Ⓑ the Blue Room

Ⓒ the Blue Office

Ⓓ the Oval Office

5. In the poem, a snail is slow because it

Ⓐ talks too much.

Ⓑ carries a house on its back.

Ⓒ has too many friends.

Ⓓ likes to rest.

6. The poem says you would be slow if you

Ⓐ did not study hard.

Ⓑ ate too much.

Ⓒ carried your house.

Ⓓ were tired.

The White House/Snail's Pace (continued)

7. The White House is the most **famous** home in America. Something **famous** is
   - Ⓐ very far away.
   - Ⓑ very old.
   - Ⓒ very well known.
   - Ⓓ very hard to find.

8. Snails **trudge.** This means they
   - Ⓐ move slowly.
   - Ⓑ carry their houses.
   - Ⓒ are always busy.
   - Ⓓ are always hungry.

Read the following question carefully. Use a complete sentence to answer the question.

9. Why do so many people visit the White House?

____

____

10. **Personal Response** Would you want to go to the White House? Why or why not?

____

____

____

____

The White House/Snail's Pace (continued)

Phonics Review

Fill in the bubble under the word that fits in the blank and is spelled correctly.

1. What will they do ________?

tlen	shen	tren	then
○	○	○	○

2. Did the ________ sail yet?

swip	stip	ship	thip
○	○	○	○

3. This is a nice ________.

clair	chair	ckair	thair
○	○	○	○

4. Ann and Jon ________ like sports.

both	borh	boch	boht
○	○	○	○

5. Paul left ________ his mother left.

wlen	twen	when	phen
○	○	○	○

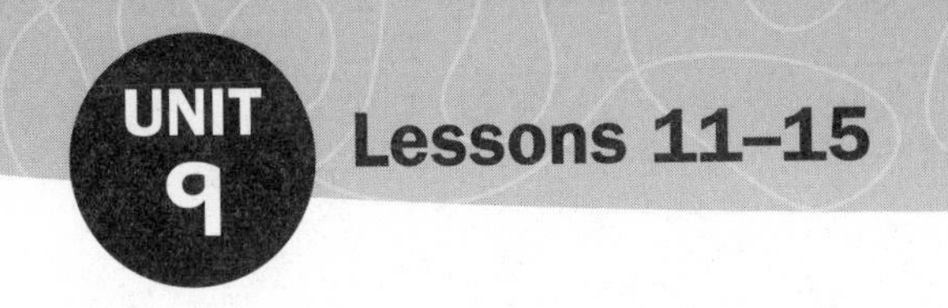

The White House/Snail's Pace (continued)

Grammar, Usage, and Mechanics

Read each item. Fill in the bubble for the answer you think is correct.

1. Which sentence is in the future tense?
   - Ⓐ Gina will go soon.
   - Ⓑ Pepe rides his bike.
   - Ⓒ Ken ate his lunch.
   - Ⓓ Judd carries a ball.

2. Which sentence is in the future tense?
   - Ⓐ Wes looks out the window.
   - Ⓑ Paula rode on the train.
   - Ⓒ Tina will ride on the bus.
   - Ⓓ Ella picks some flowers.

3. Which sentence is in the future tense?
   - Ⓐ Our team won the game.
   - Ⓑ No one lives in that house.
   - Ⓒ My friends will come to visit.
   - Ⓓ The bus waits for us.

4. Which sentence is in the future tense?
   - Ⓐ The bird flies in the air.
   - Ⓑ The cat jumps to the floor.
   - Ⓒ Dad will paint the room yellow.
   - Ⓓ Noel drank his milk.

5. Which sentence is in the future tense?
   - Ⓐ Leaves fell from the trees.
   - Ⓑ The weather is cold.
   - Ⓒ It will snow tonight.
   - Ⓓ The wind blows the snow.

The White House/Snail's Pace (continued)

Oral Fluency Assessment

Elephants

Elephants can talk. They do not use words like we use. They talk in other ways. They move their big ears. They raise their long trunks. They wave their trunks in the air.

They talk with noises they make, too. One loud sound is like a trumpet. They lift their trunks in the air. Then they make this loud sound. They also make low sounds. The low sound is like a cough. Some think it sounds like a grunt.

Mothers seem to talk to their children. The children talk back. We do not know what they are saying. People want to learn what these animals mean when they talk.

Name ______________________ Date ________ Score ________

Finding Shelter/Home

Comprehension and Vocabulary

Read the following questions carefully. Then completely fill in the bubble of each correct answer. You may look back at the selection to find the answer to each of the questions.

1. A wasp's nest is most like a

Ⓐ fish's nest.

Ⓑ spider's nest.

Ⓒ bird's nest.

Ⓓ hornet's nest.

2. What do most creatures need?

Ⓐ to find shelter from weather

Ⓑ to grow a warm coat

Ⓒ to grow their own food

Ⓓ to dig for water

3. Some animals look for a safe place in the autumn

Ⓐ to hunt.

Ⓑ to eat.

Ⓒ to fly.

Ⓓ to sleep.

Finding Shelter/Home (continued)

4. What do animals in hot places need that is different from animals in cold places?

Ⓐ thick coats
Ⓑ shady places
Ⓒ no food
Ⓓ bright sunshine

5. The poem says a home is more than just

Ⓐ fun.
Ⓑ brick.
Ⓒ shelter.
Ⓓ meal.

6. The poem is supposed to make you feel

Ⓐ tired.
Ⓑ happy.
Ⓒ mad.
Ⓓ hungry.

Finding Shelter/Home (continued)

7. A home is where you go to get **comfort. Comfort** is

Ⓐ a long walk.
Ⓑ a place for a pet.
Ⓒ a good feeling.
Ⓓ a place for a fire.

8. What is **hibernating?**

Ⓐ digging a hole
Ⓑ sleeping through the winter
Ⓒ climbing in a tall tree
Ⓓ going to a place where there is food

Read the following question carefully. Use a complete sentence to answer the question.

9. Why are people very successful animals?

____

____

10. Personal Response What animal homes are near where you live?

____

____

____

____

Finding Shelter/Home (continued)

Phonics Review

Fill in the bubble under the word that fits in the blank and is spelled correctly.

1. The horse pulled the ________.

coart	cart	ceart	cort
○	○	○	○

2. Gene has a new ________.

shert	shiirt	sheart	shirt
○	○	○	○

3. This ________ has been very cold.

wintir	winter	wintar	wintur
○	○	○	○

4. The ________ is not open.

stoor	stoar	store	stoir
○	○	○	○

5. You should ________ at the next corner.

turn	toorn	tourn	tirn
○	○	○	○

Finding Shelter/Home (continued)

Grammar, Usage, and Mechanics

Read each item. Fill in the bubble for the answer you think is correct.

1. Which sentence contains a singular noun?
   Ⓐ The children run and play.
   Ⓑ Wild animals live in zoos.
   Ⓒ The frog jumped into the water.
   Ⓓ They are afraid of snakes.

2. Which sentence contains a plural noun?
   Ⓐ Penny gave her friend a gift.
   Ⓑ Max played baseball with Deb.
   Ⓒ The girls used their bats.
   Ⓓ The log burned in the fire.

3. Which sentence contains a possessive noun?
   Ⓐ The kitten's fur is soft.
   Ⓑ The bird had blue feathers.
   Ⓒ Zebras are black and white.
   Ⓓ The room was very quiet.

4. Which sentence contains a pronoun?
   Ⓐ Nick and Lily met at the corner.
   Ⓑ They went to the park.
   Ⓒ Nick likes the slide and swings.
   Ⓓ Saturday is a busy day here.

5. Which sentence contains a possessive pronoun?
   Ⓐ Those shoes are pink.
   Ⓑ Leng won two prizes.
   Ⓒ Anton looked at the rabbits.
   Ⓓ Dad found my glove.

Finding Shelter/Home (continued)

Oral Fluency Assessment

Flowers and You

Flowers come in many colors. They have many shapes. Some are so small you can not see them. Others are quite large.

Bees like flowers. They sip sweet juice from them. Then the bees make honey. The bees also help plants grow.

Flowers turn into fruit on plants. People eat the fruit. Limes and pears are types of fruit. There are many kinds of fruit. You can see how many when you go to the store.

Seeds come from fruit. The seeds make more plants grow. If there were no flowers and seeds, we would have no new plants. And that would not be good for us.

Name ____________________ Date ________ Score ________

This House Is Made of Mud

Comprehension and Vocabulary

Read the following questions carefully. Then completely fill in the bubble of each correct answer. You may look back at the selection to find the answer to each of the questions.

1. Which of these is used to make the mud house?
   - Ⓐ wood
   - Ⓑ straw
   - Ⓒ metal
   - Ⓓ rocks

2. How is the house like the Moon?
   - Ⓐ Both are made of mud.
   - Ⓑ Both have holes.
   - Ⓒ Both have mice.
   - Ⓓ Both are round.

3. Why are there windows in the house?
   - Ⓐ So breezes can pass through
   - Ⓑ So animals can get in
   - Ⓒ So people can get in
   - Ⓓ So light can get out

This House Is Made of Mud (continued)

4. How do the mice get in the house?

Ⓐ by flying in

Ⓑ by crawling in

Ⓒ by people letting them in

Ⓓ by sliding in

5. The house's yard is

Ⓐ cool and rocky.

Ⓑ muddy and wet.

Ⓒ hot and dry.

Ⓓ very small.

6. Which of these can you infer from the story?

Ⓐ The person telling the story does not like the house.

Ⓑ The house is very famous.

Ⓒ The house is very old.

Ⓓ The person telling the story likes the house.

This House Is Made of Mud (continued)

7. The house has **tunnels** under the floor. **Tunnels** are
   Ⓐ underground passageways.
   Ⓑ tall fences to keep animals out.
   Ⓒ strong walls to keep rain out.
   Ⓓ places for a fire.

8. The family will **share** the house. To **share** means to
   Ⓐ keep for yourself.
   Ⓑ sell.
   Ⓒ give to others.
   Ⓓ visit.

Read the following question carefully. Use a complete sentence to answer the question.

9. How is the house like our Earth?

____

____

10. **Personal Response** Write about what your home is made of.

____

____

____

____

This House Is Made of Mud (continued)

Phonics Review

Fill in the bubble under the word that fits in the blank and is spelled correctly.

1. The vet will ________ the dog's coat.

clip	crip	stip	clup
○	○	○	○

2. The family is eating a ________.

mell	meol	meal	mael
○	○	○	○

3. It's time for ________.

lunsh	lunch	lanch	lunck
○	○	○	○

4. The ________ eat grass.

shep	cheip	shleep	sheep
○	○	○	○

5. Does he like to ________?

braw	drau	draw	driw
○	○	○	○

This House Is Made of Mud (continued)

Grammar, Usage, and Mechanics

Read each item. Fill in the bubble for the answer you think is correct.

1. Which sentence is in the present tense?

Ⓐ Oscar helps the teacher.
Ⓑ Jade mailed a letter.
Ⓒ Nan wanted a balloon.
Ⓓ Mrs. Miller will come soon.

2. Which sentence is in the past tense?

Ⓐ The parade begins now.
Ⓑ The mayor rides in a fancy car.
Ⓒ The band marched through town.
Ⓓ Lots of people watch the parade.

3. Which sentence is in the future tense?

Ⓐ The fire trucks will come next.
Ⓑ Everybody laughs at the clowns.
Ⓒ My brother looked for bikes.
Ⓓ These oranges taste sweet.

4. Which sentence is in the past tense?

Ⓐ Mom says the house is a mess.
Ⓑ Toni cleaned her room.
Ⓒ Dad will clean the garage.
Ⓓ The house looks nicer now.

5. Which sentence is in the future tense?

Ⓐ Helen will have a party.
Ⓑ Molly liked the party.
Ⓒ Nita wants to come, too.
Ⓓ Seth asks if he can go.

This House Is Made of Mud (continued)

Oral Fluency Assessment

Funny Rick

Nan likes music. She plays the guitar. Her dad taught her. He likes to sing when she plays.

Someone else likes the way she plays, too. It is the family dog, Rick. When Nan plays, he makes noises. It sounds like Rick is trying to sing. When he sings, Nan laughs. But Rick just keeps on singing.

Rick does other things that are funny. He loves his ball. If he wants to play, he brings you his ball. At night, he sleeps with his ball. When he goes for a walk, he takes his ball. But if you throw the ball, he will not chase it.

Name ______________________ Date ________ Score ________

Writing Prompt

Persuasive Writing

Writing Situation

How your school can be improved

Audience

The students and teachers in your school

Directions for Writing

Think of something that would make your school better. Explain why this improvement is important and why other people would like it, too.

Checklist

You will earn the best score if you

- think about your ideas before you start writing.
- tell your idea in the first sentence.
- explain why your idea is important.
- stay on the topic.
- write complete sentences.
- use words that tell how you feel about the idea.
- try to make the reader think your idea is a good one.
- repeat your idea in the last sentence.
- use correct capital letters, end marks, and spelling.
- read your writing after you finish and check for mistakes.

Name ____________________ Date ________ Score ________

My Brother Is Afraid of Just About Everything

Comprehension and Vocabulary

Read the following questions carefully. Then completely fill in the bubble of each correct answer. You may look back at the selection to find the answer to each of the questions.

1. How do we know the brother is younger?

Ⓐ He does not go to school yet.

Ⓑ He is afraid of just about everything.

Ⓒ He likes dogs.

Ⓓ He screams when water is let out of the tub.

2. The brother thinks the vacuum cleaner is

Ⓐ a bear.

Ⓑ a shark.

Ⓒ a monster.

Ⓓ a lion.

3. Where does the brother go during a storm?

Ⓐ behind the bushes

Ⓑ under the bed

Ⓒ into the bathtub

Ⓓ in his closet

My Brother Is Afraid of Just About Everything (continued)

4. Why does the brother wrap his arms around the sister?

Ⓐ He is pretending to be a snake.
Ⓑ He is afraid of the train.
Ⓒ He loves the sister very much.
Ⓓ He needs to hold the sister up.

5. How is the sister like the brother?

Ⓐ Both are afraid of dogs.
Ⓑ Both are afraid of the vacuum cleaner.
Ⓒ Both are afraid of school.
Ⓓ Both are afraid of something.

6. Why is the brother happy?

Ⓐ He gets to go to school.
Ⓑ He sees a dog.
Ⓒ He sees a train.
Ⓓ He sees some friends.

My Brother Is Afraid of Just About Everything (continued)

7. Another word for **underneath** is
   - Ⓐ below.
   - Ⓑ afraid.
   - Ⓒ thunderstorm.
   - Ⓓ away.

8. **Trembling** means about the same as
   - Ⓐ jumping.
   - Ⓑ crying.
   - Ⓒ smiling.
   - Ⓓ shaking.

Read the following question carefully. Use a complete sentence to answer the question.

9. Why is the brother afraid of so many things?

____

____

10. **Personal Response** Write about something you are afraid of.

____

____

____

____

My Brother Is Afraid of Just About Everything **(continued)**

Phonics Review

Fill in the bubble under the word that fits in the blank and is spelled correctly.

1. This desk is made of ________.

wode	woed	wood	wod
○	○	○	○

2. This is Pam's ________.

bok	book	boak	bowk
○	○	○	○

3. Tom put the ball in the ________.

houp	hupe	hoip	hoop
○	○	○	○

4. Jan's dog got ________.

loose	loos	loise	lowse
○	○	○	○

5. The plant ________ bigger.

groo	grou	grew	griw
○	○	○	○

My Brother Is Afraid of Just About Everything (continued)

Grammar, Usage, and Mechanics

Read each item. Fill in the bubble for the answer you think is correct.

1. Which sentence has a comparative adjective?

Ⓐ The goats ate the grass.
Ⓑ Many people watch funny movies.
Ⓒ Raoul plays music louder than Beth.
Ⓓ The chair is big and soft.

2. In which sentence is the underlined part correct?

Ⓐ Jane is tall than anyone else in class.
Ⓑ Jane is taller than anyone else in class.
Ⓒ Jane is tallest than anyone else in class.
Ⓓ Jane is more taller than anyone else in class.

3. Which word means about the same as pleased?

Ⓐ strong
Ⓑ afraid
Ⓒ glad
Ⓓ busy

4. Which word means about the same as finish?

Ⓐ ride
Ⓑ end
Ⓒ play
Ⓓ look

5. Which word means the opposite of small?

Ⓐ large
Ⓑ new
Ⓒ hard
Ⓓ weak

My Brother Is Afraid of Just About Everything (continued)

Oral Fluency Assessment

The Noise Outside

Anne and Mr. Rojas went outside. They had heard a strange noise. They looked to see what it was. They could not find anything.

"Let's go back in, Anne. We can look later if we hear the sound again."

"I want to look near that bush. Then I will come in."

Anne went to the bush at the far side of the house. It was dark, and she could not see well. Just then, something furry crawled up against her face. Anne almost jumped out of her skin! Then she saw what it was.

"Dad! Dad! Remember when you said I could have a kitten? I think my kitten just found me."

Name ______________________ Date __________ Score __________

There's a Big Beautiful World Out There!/Night Comes

Comprehension and Vocabulary

Read the following questions carefully. Then completely fill in the bubble of each correct answer. You may look back at the selection to find the answer to each of the questions.

1. The story says that hiding under the covers
   - Ⓐ is the best thing to do.
   - Ⓑ makes you hungry.
   - Ⓒ can be scary.
   - Ⓓ gets boring.

2. The dog in the story
   - Ⓐ is big and runs fast.
   - Ⓑ looks mean but might be nice.
   - Ⓒ has spots and is small.
   - Ⓓ likes to bark and howl.

3. In the story, who will say everything will be all right?
   - Ⓐ sister
   - Ⓑ brother
   - Ⓒ mother
   - Ⓓ father

There's a Big Beautiful World Out There!/Night Comes (continued)

4. The story says you will miss out on the big beautiful world if you

Ⓐ go outside.

Ⓑ read the news.

Ⓒ ride a roller coaster.

Ⓓ hide under the covers.

5. Which of these is NOT in "Night Comes"?

Ⓐ stars

Ⓑ moon

Ⓒ clouds

Ⓓ night

6. The person who wrote "Night Comes"

Ⓐ is sleeping.

Ⓑ is a little hungry.

Ⓒ is tired.

Ⓓ is not afraid.

There's a Big Beautiful World Out There!/Night Comes (continued)

7. The stars come **peeking**. What does **peeking** mean?

Ⓐ looking quickly
Ⓑ hiding behind clouds
Ⓒ staring for a long time
Ⓓ smiling down

8. A **solo** can make you feel good. What is a **solo?**

Ⓐ jumping high
Ⓑ playing hard
Ⓒ running or walking fast
Ⓓ singing or playing alone

Read the following question carefully. Use a complete sentence to answer the question.

9. What does the story want you to do?

____

____

10. Personal Response Write about something you used to be afraid of.

____

____

____

____

There's a Big Beautiful World Out There!/Night Comes (continued)

Phonics Review

Fill in the bubble under the word that fits in the blank and is spelled correctly.

1. May I play with that ________?

toy	tou	tey	toie
○	○	○	○

2. Did the water ________ yet?

bool	boil	boyl	bowle
○	○	○	○

3. A lion's roar is ________.

lood	loud	lowd	luod
○	○	○	○

4. Bill lives in ________.

toon	toiwn	touen	town
○	○	○	○

5. Open your ________ wide.

meuth	mowth	mouth	moith
○	○	○	○

There's a Big Beautiful World Out There!/Night Comes (continued)

Grammar, Usage, and Mechanics

Read each item. Fill in the bubble for the answer you think is correct.

1. Which of these is a declarative sentence?

Ⓐ Is this your pet?
Ⓑ Don't do that.
Ⓒ Sue kicks the ball.
Ⓓ She scored a goal!

2. Which of these is an interrogative sentence?

Ⓐ Is it time to leave?
Ⓑ Ross wants to play, too.
Ⓒ Let Andy bat first.
Ⓓ The game is almost over.

3. Which of these is an exclamatory sentence?

Ⓐ Do you know her name?
Ⓑ I can't wait!
Ⓒ The train comes at five o'clock.
Ⓓ Her pencil is new.

4. Which of these is an imperative sentence?

Ⓐ Pick up that trash now.
Ⓑ Julie wants Hannah for her team.
Ⓒ Who is on the other team?
Ⓓ The path goes to the beach.

5. Which of these is a declarative sentence?

Ⓐ Please help Rita carry that.
Ⓑ Where is the train station?
Ⓒ Phan packed her bags.
Ⓓ Does that store sell books?

There's a Big Beautiful World Out There!/Night Comes (continued)

Oral Fluency Assessment

A Helpful Ship

A tug is small boat. It does an important job. It helps big ships. Big ships carry things across the seas. They have to go close to shore to unload. The big ships must sail into small places. They do not know the places well. They could run into danger.

The tug can push or pull the big ship. It will help the ship get to the dock. The tug will make sure nothing bad happens.

Tugs are strong and work hard. A small tug can move a big ship. With the help of a tug, a large ship will get into the harbor and finish its job.

Name ______________________ Date ________ Score ________

Clyde Monster/The Cat and the Mice

Comprehension and Vocabulary

Read the following questions carefully. Then completely fill in the bubble of each correct answer. You may look back at the selection to find the answer to each of the questions.

1. You know the story is not real because
   - Ⓐ monsters are not clumsy.
   - Ⓑ monsters are not ugly.
   - Ⓒ monsters do not exist.
   - Ⓓ monsters do turn somersaults.

2. What is Clyde afraid of?
   - Ⓐ dogs
   - Ⓑ people
   - Ⓒ loud noises
   - Ⓓ bright lights

3. Something that is real and not make-believe in the story is
   - Ⓐ a pretty monster.
   - Ⓑ a family of monsters.
   - Ⓒ being able to breathe fire.
   - Ⓓ being afraid of the dark.

Clyde Monster/The Cat and the Mice (continued)

4. Clyde is different because he is

Ⓐ hungrier than other monsters.

Ⓑ funnier than other monsters.

Ⓒ clumsier than other monsters.

Ⓓ scarier than other monsters.

5. Why is the cat chasing the mice?

Ⓐ The cat is sad.

Ⓑ The cat wants to play.

Ⓒ The cat has no friends.

Ⓓ The cat is hungry.

6. No one answers the oldest mouse's question because

Ⓐ the mice are too scared.

Ⓑ no one heard it.

Ⓒ the question is too hard.

Ⓓ they are afraid of the oldest mouse.

Clyde Monster/The Cat and the Mice (continued)

7. Many mice had something to **suggest.** To **suggest** means to
   Ⓐ say.
   Ⓑ run.
   Ⓒ hide.
   Ⓓ sleep.

8. Monsters are **usually** ugly. **Usually** means
   Ⓐ most of the time.
   Ⓑ in a dark room.
   Ⓒ only when angry.
   Ⓓ never.

Read the following question carefully. Use a complete sentence to answer the question.

9. What does Clyde's father show him?

____

____

10. **Personal Response** What do you do to feel safe at night?

____

____

____

____

Clyde Monster/The Cat and the Mice (continued)

Phonics Review

Fill in the bubble under the word that fits in the blank and is spelled correctly.

1. Ben ________ his shoe.

intiez	ontiez	unties	anties
○	○	○	○

2. Ana ________ first.

batted	baated	batd	batteed
○	○	○	○

3. Are you ________ me?

askking	asking	askng	askiing
○	○	○	○

4. Thank you for your ________.

kindnss	kindeness	kindness	kindnes
○	○	○	○

5. This story has two ________.

parttes	partts	partes	parts
○	○	○	○

Clyde Monster/The Cat and the Mice (continued)

Grammar, Usage, and Mechanics

Read each item. Fill in the bubble for the answer you think is correct.

1. Which sentence has correct capitalization?

Ⓐ Can i go along with you?
Ⓑ Aunt Rita wants to leave.
Ⓒ that's Riverside School.
Ⓓ The game is on monday.

2. Which sentence has correct capitalization?

Ⓐ Grandpa lives in Denver, Colorado.
Ⓑ Grandma sent a package to florida.
Ⓒ did you ever visit Africa?
Ⓓ My friend's family is from korea.

3. Which sentence has correct capitalization?

Ⓐ our first game is on monday.
Ⓑ His Birthday is on sunday.
Ⓒ My birthday is in April.
Ⓓ The first snow was in november.

4. Which sentence has correct punctuation?

Ⓐ Dad was born on April 24, 1973.
Ⓑ Dad was born on April 24 1973.
Ⓒ Dad was born on April, 24 1973.
Ⓓ Dad was born on April, 24, 1973.

5. Which sentence has correct capitalization and punctuation?

Ⓐ Flora lives in austin, Texas.
Ⓑ Flora lives in Austin, Texas.
Ⓒ Flora lives in Austin texas.
Ⓓ Flora lives in austin, texas.

Clyde Monster/The Cat and the Mice (continued)

Oral Fluency Assessment

Rainy Day

It was a rainy day. The children were sad. They could not go out to play. They had to stay home. They did not know what they would do. They sat around bored.

Mom saw how unhappy they were. She told them not to forget what they could do inside. They could read books. They could play games. Maybe they could watch a movie. The children said that would be fun.

Soon Mom made lunch. The children imagined it was a picnic. They ate on the porch. They put a blanket down to make it seem real.

The sun soon came out. But no one noticed. They were having fun inside.

Name ______________________ Date __________ Score __________

Ira Sleeps Over

Comprehension and Vocabulary

Read the following questions carefully. Then completely fill in the bubble of each correct answer. You may look back at the selection to find the answer to each of the questions.

1. This story is mostly about
   - Ⓐ things that are fun to do at a sleep-over.
   - Ⓑ why boys like teddy bears.
   - Ⓒ a boy who sleeps over at a friend's house.
   - Ⓓ two boys who want the same toy.

2. What does Ira do right after Reggie said "Foo Foo"?
   - Ⓐ He tells a scary story about ghosts.
   - Ⓑ He tries to wake up Reggie.
   - Ⓒ He falls asleep.
   - Ⓓ He goes home and gets his teddy bear.

3. Ira does not take his teddy bear to Reggie's house because
   - Ⓐ he thinks Reggie will laugh.
   - Ⓑ the bear is too big.
   - Ⓒ his sister will tease him.
   - Ⓓ Reggie says he has a bear.

Ira Sleeps Over (continued)

4. Why is Ira excited at the start of the story?

Ⓐ He gets a brand new toy.

Ⓑ He will be doing something new.

Ⓒ He meets a new friend.

Ⓓ He is going to a new school.

5. Which of these is true about Ira's sister?

Ⓐ She thinks Ira is tall.

Ⓑ She knows Reggie well.

Ⓒ She takes care of Ira.

Ⓓ She likes to tease Ira.

6. What is the name of Ira's teddy bear?

Ⓐ Foo Foo

Ⓑ Tah Tah

Ⓒ Reggie

Ⓓ Aroomp

Ira Sleeps Over (continued)

7. The boys wanted to have a wrestling **match.** A **match** is a kind of
   - Ⓐ game.
   - Ⓑ toy.
   - Ⓒ book.
   - Ⓓ bed.

8. Ira **changed his mind.** This means he
   - Ⓐ wanted something to eat.
   - Ⓑ did something different.
   - Ⓒ worried about something.
   - Ⓓ had a lot of fun.

Read the following question carefully. Use a complete sentence to answer the question.

9. Why does Ira decide it is okay to go and get his teddy bear?

____

____

10. **Personal Response** What do you have that is like Ira's teddy bear?

____

____

____

Ira Sleeps Over (continued)

Phonics Review

Fill in the bubble under the word that fits in the blank and is spelled correctly.

1. Will Kara go ________ you?

wint	wigh	wich	with
○	○	○	○

2. Peg lives ________ the park.

nerr	near	neer	nair
○	○	○	○

3. My brother lost one ________.

sock	soct	sosk	soch
○	○	○	○

4. That ________ is loud.

sound	sownd	soind	soond
○	○	○	○

5. Jim ________ his cat outside.

toik	touk	took	tok
○	○	○	○

Ira Sleeps Over (continued)

Grammar, Usage, and Mechanics

Read each item. Fill in the bubble for the answer you think is correct.

1. Which of these means the same as are not?

Ⓐ isn't
Ⓑ aren't
Ⓒ don't
Ⓓ can't

2. Which of these means the same as they will?

Ⓐ they'
Ⓑ they're
Ⓒ they'll
Ⓓ we'll

3. Which of these means the same as you are?

Ⓐ you're
Ⓑ you'll
Ⓒ he'll
Ⓓ we're

4. Which of these means the same as would not?

Ⓐ won't
Ⓑ wasn't
Ⓒ wouldn't
Ⓓ we'll

5. Which of these means the same as he is?

Ⓐ she'll
Ⓑ he's
Ⓒ he'd
Ⓓ it's

Ira Sleeps Over (continued)

Oral Fluency Assessment

A Sense of Smell

Dogs have good noses. Dogs can smell things that people can not smell. They use their noses to find food.

Sometimes dogs help find people who are lost. They follow them by sniffing the trail. They put their noses low to the ground. They smell where the people walked. Dogs help to save lots of people. They can find animals, too.

Dogs learned to smell well long ago. It helped them find food. It helped them find other dogs. A group of dogs is called a pack. If a dog was lost, it could smell the pack. Then the dog could find its way home.

Name ______________________ Date ________ Score ________

Writing Prompt

Narrative Writing

Writing Situation

Your own adventure story

Audience

Other students your age

Directions for Writing

Write your own adventure story. It can be in a real or imaginary setting like a different planet or a time in the past. Your story should have interesting characters and an exciting plot.

Checklist

You will earn the best score if you

- think about your ideas before you start writing.
- stay on topic.
- have a good beginning, middle, and end to your story.
- tell about the place where the story happens.
- tell about the characters in your story.
- write complete sentences.
- use words that tell how the characters feel.
- include enough details so the reader will understand what happened.
- use correct capital letters, end marks, and spelling.
- read your writing after you finish and check for mistakes.